I Can Do It Myself!

60 More Beginning Skills Activity Sheets

BY ROSIE SEAMAN

ILLUSTRATED BY JANE CAMINOS

Fearon Teacher Aids

Editor: Susan Eddy

Fearon Teacher Aids
An Imprint of Modern Curriculum
A Division of Simon & Schuster
299 Jefferson Road, P.O. Box 480
Parsippany, NJ 07054-0480

3 4 5 6 7 8 9   TCS   04 03 02 01 00 99 98 97 96

Contents

INTRODUCTION

Children love to use their hands. The skills they acquire in eye-hand coordination through such activities as tracing, coloring, cutting, and pasting create the foundation for the development of more refined abilities and skills.

This book of worksheets has been designed to develop these early skills—fine-motor coordination as well as cognitive recognition of letters and numbers. The book is divided into three sections: "Sounds and Letters," "Numbers and Counting," and "Color, Cut, Paste."

Writing practice is provided for both upper and lowercase letters, and numbers to 10. Children may trace the progressively lighter letters or numbers. Space is provided for them to make letters or numbers on their own as well.

Activities require minimal adult supervision. You will need some basic tools (blunt scissors, crayons, and glue) and a few "extras," such as colorful yarn and cotton balls. Enjoy the activities!

I Can Bob for Apples

Trace the dotted lines.
Color the picture.
Trace the letters.
Say the name of
   the letter.

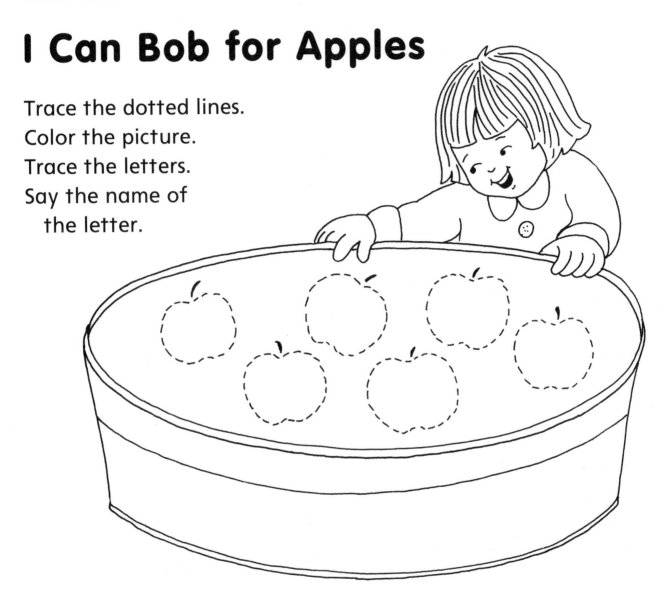

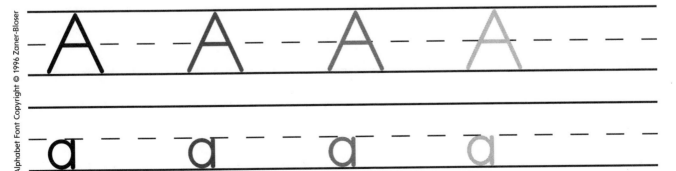

Alphabet Font Copyright © 1996 Zaner-Bloser

5

Name _____

I Can Put Animals in the Barn

Draw some farm animals.
Color your picture.
Trace the letters.
Say the name of the letter.

B - - - B - - - B - - - B

b - - - b - - - b - - - b

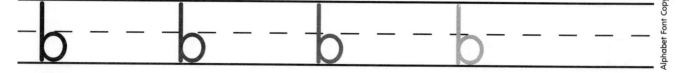

Name _____

I Can Dress Clark the Clown

Color Clark and his clothes.
Paste Clark on posterboard and
  cut him out.
Cut out his clothes and dress him.
Trace the letters.
Say the name of the letter.

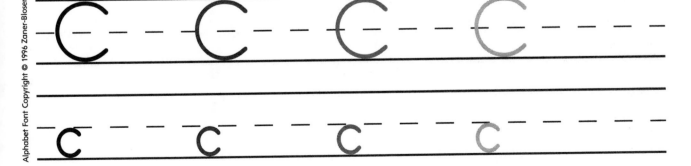

Name _____

I Can Help Feed Don the Dog

Trace the dotted lines.
Color the picture.
Trace the letters.
Say the name
  of the letter.

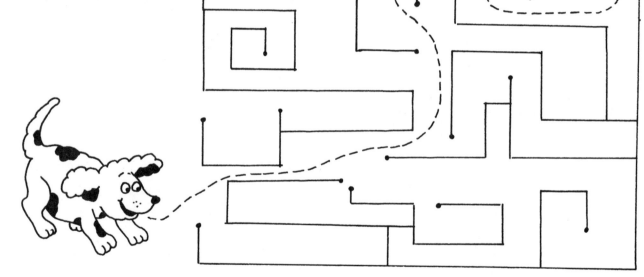

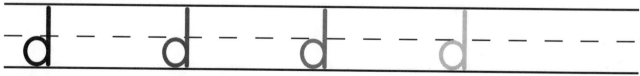

Alphabet Font Copyright © 1996 Zaner-Bloser

Name _____

I Can Train the Elephant

Trace the dotted lines.
Color the picture.
Trace the letters.
Say the name of the letter.

E — E — E — E

e   e   e   e

Name _____

I Can Catch the Football

Trace the dotted lines.
Color the picture.
Trace the letters.
Say the name of the letter.

F — F — F — F — F — F —

f — f — f — f — f — f —

Name _____

I Can Put the Horse Behind the Gate

Trace the dotted lines.
Color the picture.
Trace the letters.
Say the name of the letter.

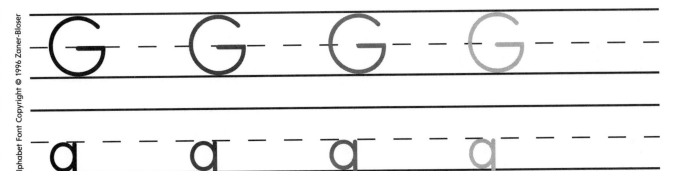

G — G — G — G

g — g — g — g

Name _____

I Can Color the Community Workers' Hats

Do you know who wears
  these hats to work?
Color the hats.
Trace the letters.
Say the name
  of the letter.

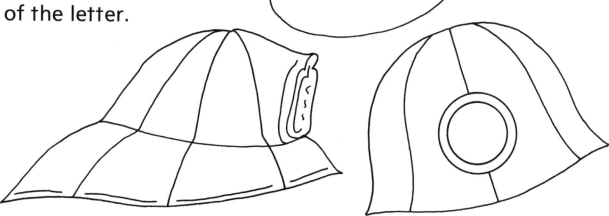

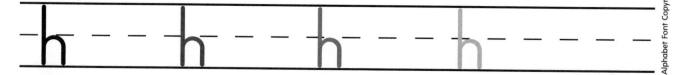

Alphabet Font Copyright © 1996 Zaner-Bloser

Name _____

I Can Build a Canoe
for the American Indian

Trace the dotted lines.
Color the picture.
Trace the letters.
Say the name
   of the letter.

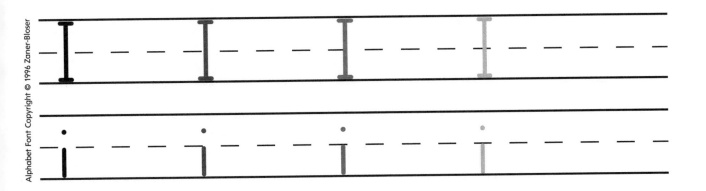

I Can Put Bugs in a Jar

Cut out the bugs.
Paste the bugs in the jar.
Trace the letters.
Say the name
of the letter.

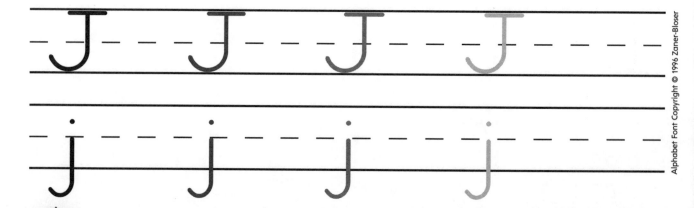

Name _____

I Can Crown the King

Trace the dotted lines.
Color the picture.
Trace the letters.
Say the name
   of the letter.

K — K — K — K

k — k — k — k

Name _____

I Can Put a Stamp on the Letter

Cut out the stamp.
Paste it on the letter.
Trace the letters.
Say the name
   of the letter.

Laura Lyons
123 Lemon Tree Lane
Lanford, Louisiana
70123

Name _____

I Can Print My Name
on the Mailbox

Trace the dotted lines.
Print your name on
the mailbox.
Color the picture.
Trace the letters.
Say the name of
the letter.

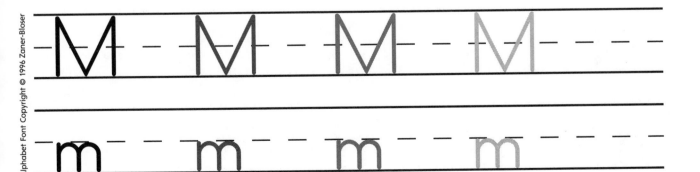

I Can See the Moon and Stars at Night

Cut out the moon and stars.
Paste the moon and stars in the sky.
Color the night scene.
Trace the letters.
Say the name of the letter.

N N N N N

n n n n

Name _____

I Can Color Ollie the Owl

Trace the dotted lines.
Color the picture.
Trace the letters.
Say the name of the letter.

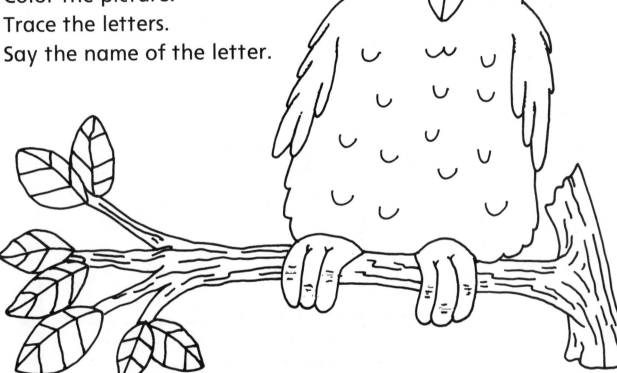

Alphabet Font Copyright © 1996 Zaner-Bloser

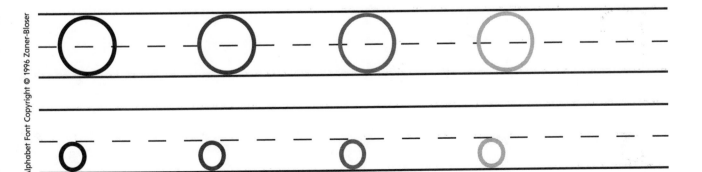

19

I Can Finish Pam's Portrait

Trace the dotted lines
  to complete
  Pam's portrait.
Color the picture
  frame.
Trace the letters.
Say the name
  of the letter.

P   P   P   P

p   p   p   p

Name _____

I Can Design a Dress for the Queen

The queen has a crown on her head and fancy slippers on her feet.
Design a dress to complete her outfit.
Trace the letters.
Say the name of the letter.

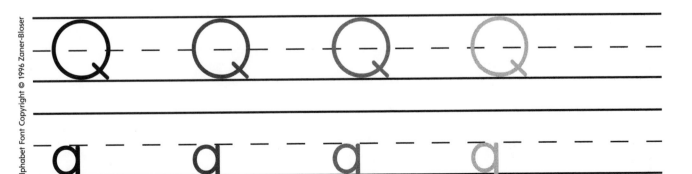

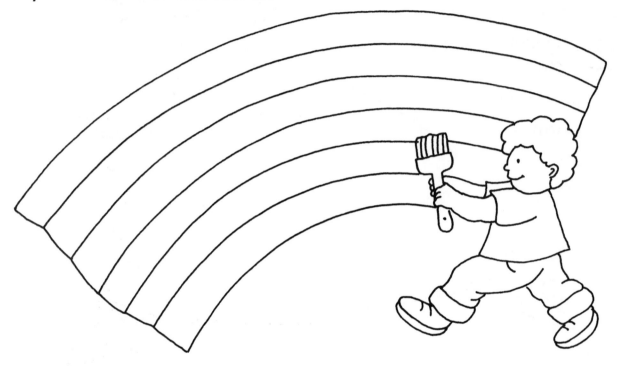

Name _____

I Can Paint the Rainbow

Color each space on the rainbow
   a different color.
Trace the letters.
Say the name of the letter.

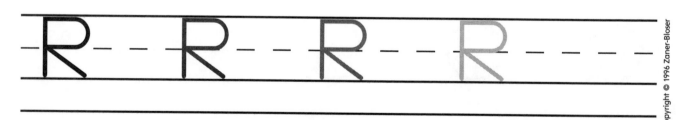

Alphabet Font Copyright © 1996 Zaner-Bloser

©1996 Fearon Teacher Aids

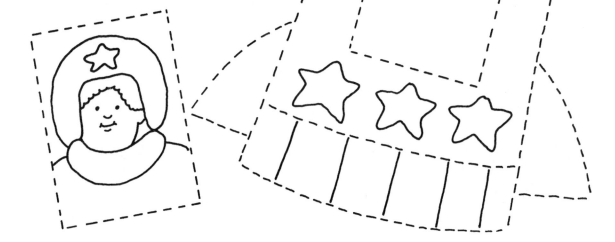

I Can Put Sam in Space

Trace the dotted lines.
Color the spaceship.
Cut out Sam and glue him
   in place on the spaceship.
Trace the letters.
Say the name of the letter.

I Can Put Wheels on the Tractor

Trace the dotted lines.
Color the picture.
Trace the letters.
Say the name
   of the letter.

I Can Make a Handle for the Umbrella

Trace the dotted lines.
Color the picture.
Trace the letters.
Say the name of
the letter.

Alphabet Font Copyright © 1996 Zaner-Bloser

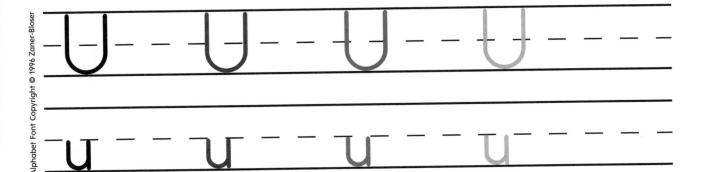

I Can Put Flowers in the Vase

Trace the dotted lines.
Color the picture.
Trace the letters.
Say the name of
    the letter.

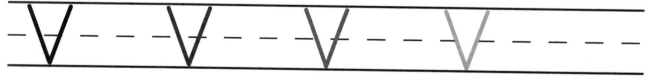

I Can Look Through the Window

What would you like to see
  out the window?
Draw it in the picture.
Color the picture.
Trace the letters.
Say the name of the letter.

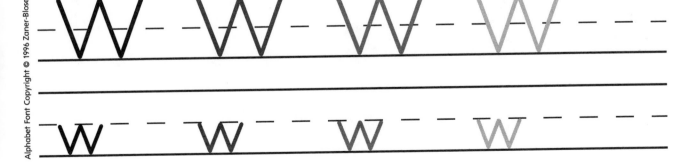

Alphabet Font Copyright © 1996 Zaner-Bloser

Name _____

I Can Make Sticks for the Xylophone

Trace the dotted lines.
Color each part of the xylophone
 a different color.
Trace the letters.
Say the name of the letter.

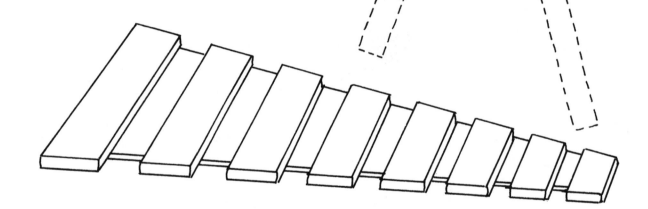

X — — X — X — X

X X X X

Alphabet Font Copyright © 1996 Zaner-Bloser

I Can Color the Sunflowers Yellow

There are some hidden
sunflowers in this picture.
Find all the sunflowers and
color them yellow.
Color the picture.
Trace the letters.
Say the name of the letter.

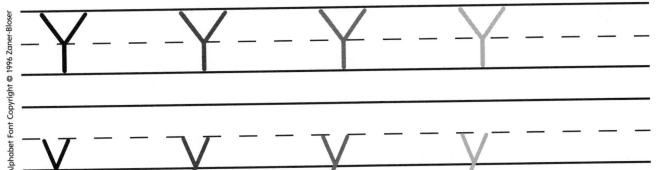

Y   Y   Y   Y

y   y   y   y

Alphabet Font Copyright © 1996 Zaner-Bloser

Name _____

I Can Visit the Zoo

There are many animals at the zoo.
Draw your favorite animal.
Color the picture.
Trace the letters.
Say the name of the letter.

Alphabet Font Copyright © 1996 Zaner-Bloser

I Can Say the Alphabet From A to Z

Say the name of each letter
   as you follow the dots.
Begin with letter **A** and
   end with the letter **Z**.
Color the picture.

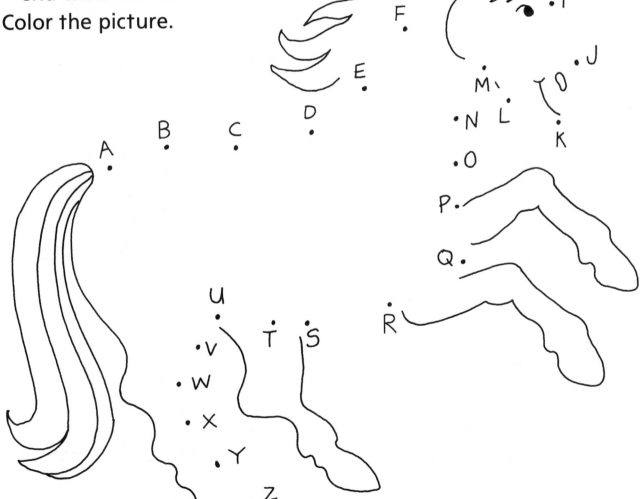

I Can Print the Alphabet From A to Z

Trace the dotted lines.
Print the missing letters.
Start with letter **A**.
Color the picture.

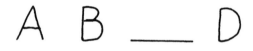

A   B   __   D
E   __   G   __
I   J   __   L
__   N   O   __   __
R   S   __   U   __
W   __   Y   Z

I Can Name the Toys

Say the name of each toy.
Listen to the beginning sound.
Finish printing each toy's name
  under its picture.
Color the toys.

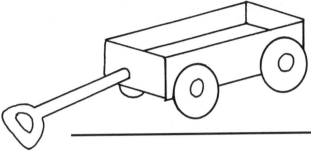

agon

rain

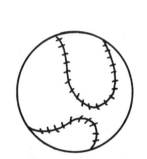

o-yo

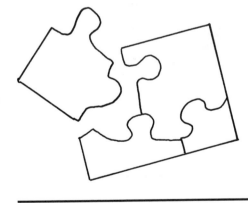

uzzle

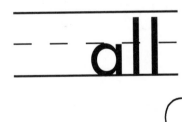

all

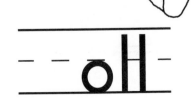

oll

Name _____

I Can Play
Letter Game 1

What animal gives you the milk
  you drink?
Print the beginning letter of each
  picture to find the answer.
Color the pictures.

Name _____

I Can Play
Letter Game 2

What does grandma bake that
   smells so good?
Print the beginning letter of each
   picture to find the answer.
Color the pictures.

I Can Play
Letter Game 3

What shines brightly from the sky
  and lights up the day?
Print the beginning letter under
  each picture to find the answer.
Color the pictures.

I Can Color the Earth

Trace the dotted lines.
Color the water blue and
   the land green.
Trace the number **1**.
Say the number.
How many earths
   are there?

Land

Land

Land

Land

Water

Land

Land

Water

I Can Put the Birds in the Cage

Trace the dotted lines.
Color the picture.
Trace the number **2**.
Say the number.
How many birds
   are there?

2 — 2 — 2 — 2 —

Name _____

I Can Count the Planes in the Sky

Trace the dotted lines.
Color the pictures.
Glue cotton on the clouds.
Trace the number **3**.
Say the number.
How many planes are there?

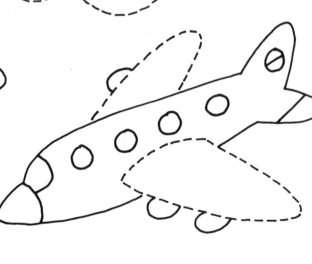

3 - - 3 - - 3 - - 3 - - - -

I Can Cut the Pizza Into Slices

Trace the dotted lines.
Color the pizza.
Trace the number **4**.
Say the number.
How many slices of
   pizza are there?

4 — 4 — 4 — 4

Alphabet Font Copyright © 1996 Zaner-Bloser

Name _____

I Can Help Frank Feed the Goldfish

Trace the dotted lines.
Color the picture.
Trace the number **5**.
Say the number.
How many goldfish
   are there?

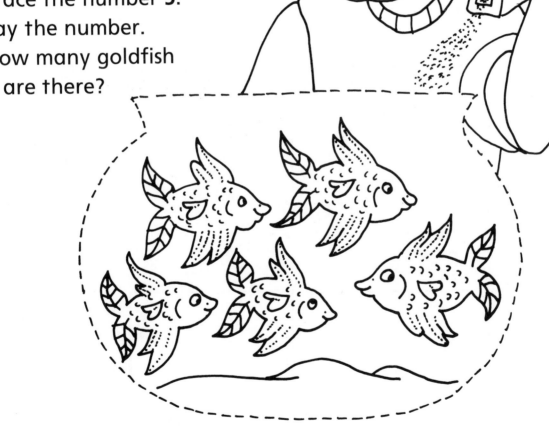

5 — 5 — 5 — 5

Name _____

I Can Tell a Story About Pat the Puppy

Look at the pictures.
Do you know what happened?
Use the numbers to tell the story
   from beginning to end.
Cut them out and paste them in place.

1 **2** **3** **4**

Name _____

I Can Count the Farm Animals

Look at the picture.
How many farm animals can
   you count?
Print the correct number
   under each group of animals.

I Can Circle the Smallest Number

Look at each fish.
Circle the smallest number
  in each fish.
Color the picture.

5 3 1

3 2 1

2 4 3

3 1 4

5 4 3

) 3 5 4

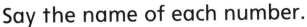

Name _____

I Can Color the Elephant in the Jungle

Look at each number in the jungle picture.
Color each space according to the color code.
Say the name of each number.

1–gray
2–green
3–red
4–yellow
5–blue

Name _____

I Can Have Fun With Fingerprints

Turn the fingerprints into six
   different things.
Maybe you can make a bug
   or a balloon.
Trace the number **6**.
Say the number.

6 — 6 — 6 — 6

Alphabet Font Copyright © 1996 Zaner-Bloser

I Can Help Ruth the Rabbit Find the Eggs

Follow the dotted lines.
Begin with Ruth the Rabbit.
Trace the number **7**.
Say the number.
How many eggs did Ruth the
   Rabbit find on her way home?

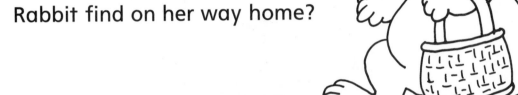

Name _____

I Can Count the Spots on the Dog

Trace the dotted lines.
Color the picture.
Trace the number **8**.
Say the number.
How many spots are
   on the dog?

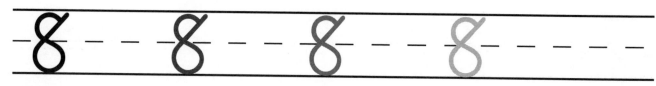

Name _____

I Can Pick the Oranges Off the Tree

Trace the dotted lines.
Color the picture.
Trace the number 9.
Say the number.
How many oranges
   are on the tree?

9 _ _ 9 _ _ 9 _ _ 9

49

I Can Fill the Machine With Bubble Gum

Trace the dotted lines.
Color the picture.
Trace the number **10**.
Say the number.
How many pieces
  of bubble gum
  are there?

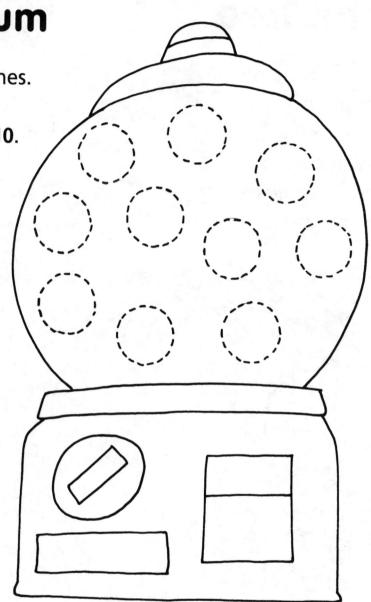

Alphabet Font Copyright © 1996 Zaner-Bloser

10 – 10 – 10 – 10

Name _____

I Can Circle the Largest Number

Look at each carrot.
Circle the largest number in
  each carrot.
Color the picture.

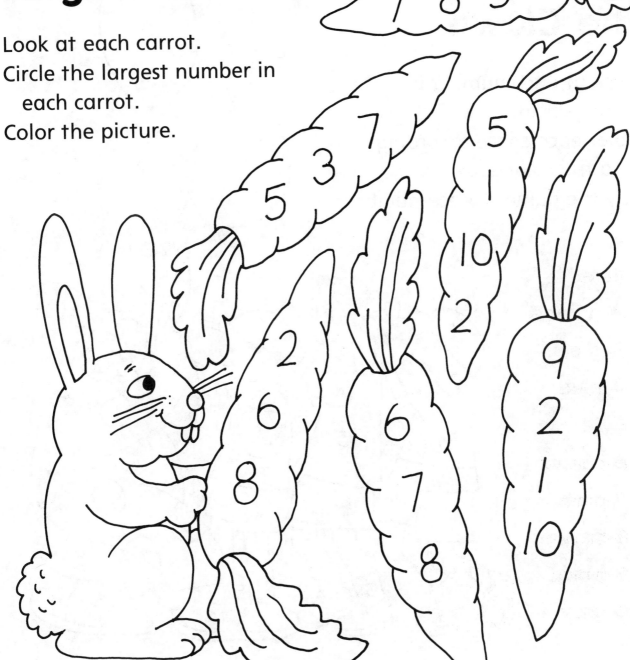

51

I Can Color the Balloons for the Clown

Look at each number in
  the picture.
Color each space according
  to the color code.
Say the name of each number.

1–red

2–orange

3–green

4–blue

5–yellow

6–purple

7–pink

8–brown

9–black

10–gray

Name _____

Name _____

I Can Print My Numbers From 1 to 10

Trace the dotted-line.
Can you help the teacher print
  the numbers from 1 to 10?
Color the picture.

Name _____

I Can Build a Boat to Sail

Follow the dots from 1 to 10.
Draw yourself inside the boat.
Be sure to put on a life jacket!
Color the picture.

I Can Feed the Elephant

Elephants love to eat peanuts.
Draw 10 peanuts for the elephant
   inside the bag.
Color the picture.

I Can Count the Flowers

Look at each picture.
How many flowers can you find?
Print the correct number
   under each picture.
Color the picture.

Name _____

I Can Fix the Broken Cars

Cut out the broken cars.
Match the pieces.
Glue them together on a
    sheet of construction paper.
Color the two cars when
    the glue is dry.

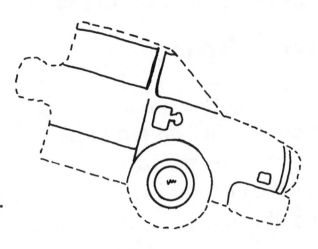

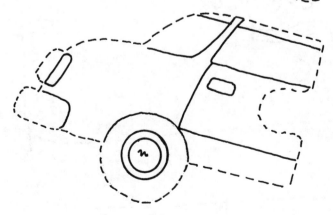

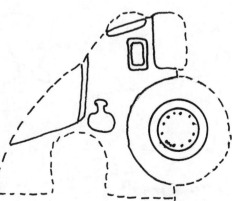

I Can Decorate the Cake

Trace the dotted lines.
Cut out the smiling sun faces.
Paste them on the cake.
Color the picture when
   the glue is dry.

Name _____

I Can Set the Table for Dinner

Lend a helping hand.
Trace the dotted lines.
Color your place mat.
Draw your favorite dinner
    on the plate.

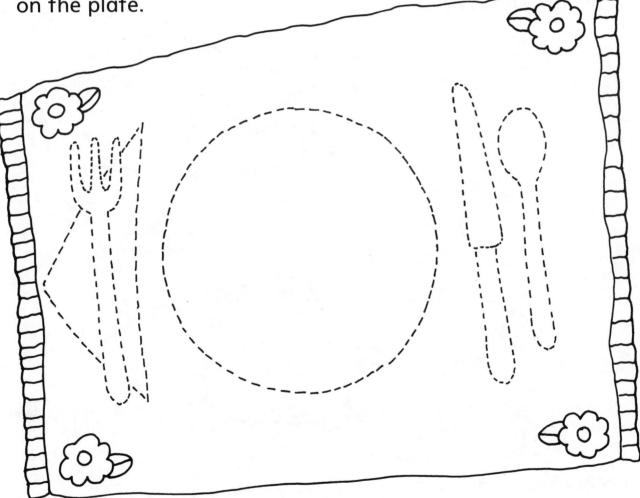

Name _____

I Can Make Some Silly Creatures

Here is a body of a cat and a body
   of a dog.
Draw on each body the other
   animal's tail, feet, and ears.
Color your silly creatures.

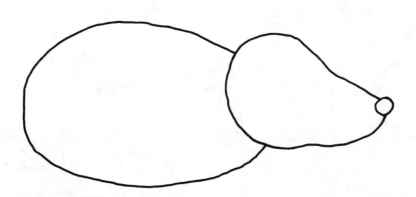

Name _____

I Can Fill the Grocery Cart With Food

Be a wise shopper.
Cut out the foods and paste them
   in the grocery cart.
Color the picture when it is dry.

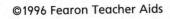

Name _____

I Can Put the Animal Cookies Together

Cut out the broken cookies.
Paste them together on a sheet
   of construction paper.
Color the three animal cookies
   when they are dry.
Say the name of each animal.

Name _____

I Can Put the Fruit in the Basket

Trace the dotted lines.
Cut out the bow.
Paste it on the top of
the basket.
Color the picture.

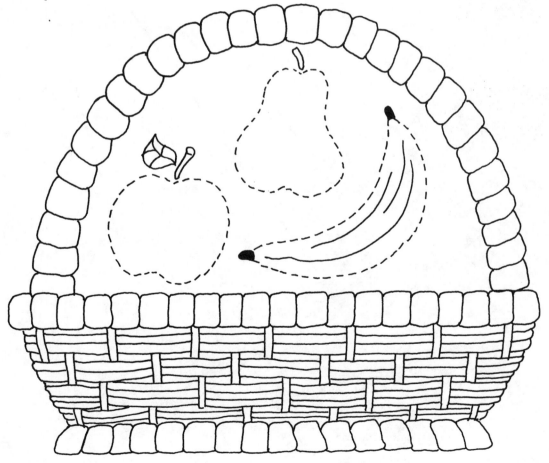

I Can Make a Pennant
for My Bedroom Door

Print your name on the pennant.
Color and cut out the pennant.
Tape it to the door of your bedroom.